SCISSOR SKILLS

A PRESCHOOL WORKBOOK FOR KIDS

THIS BOOK BELONGS TO:

_____

. . . .

_____

WANT FREE GOODIES?!

Email us at

modernkidpress@gmail.com

Title the email "Scissor Skills!"
and we'll send some goodies
your way!

Questions & Customer Service:
Email us at modernkidpress@gmail.com!

SCISSOR SKILLS

WHY ARE SCISSOR SKILLS IMPORTANT?

Learning to use scissors correctly is an important skill for young children to learn. When you open and close scissors using the muscles in your hand you are practicing fine motor skills. Fine motor skills are essential for when children begin to learn to write.

Learning to use scissors also helps children develop hand-eye coordination. Holding the scissors in one hand and the paper in the other, children will practice watching and guiding the scissors as they move across the paper.

TIPS

Teaching scissor skills can be frustrating for parents and kids. Take a deep breath and set yourself up for success with these tips!

1. **Talk to your child about scissor safety.** Explain that scissors are ONLY for cutting paper. Nothing else! Also stress the importance of not walking with scissors.

2. **Get a good set of scissors.** It is best to start with scissors that have a blunt point, however, make sure they aren't too dull and that they are sharp enough to cut the paper.

3. **Help your child correctly hold the scissors.** If your child is left handed, be sure to purchase left handed scissors.

Start slow and remember...practice makes progress!!

THE FLOWER STEMS

Practice cutting straight lines as you cut along each flower stem.

LET'S CUT ALONG:
TRAIN TRACKS

Practice cutting straight lines as you cut along each train track.

BALLOONS

Practice cutting curvy lines as you cut along each balloon string.

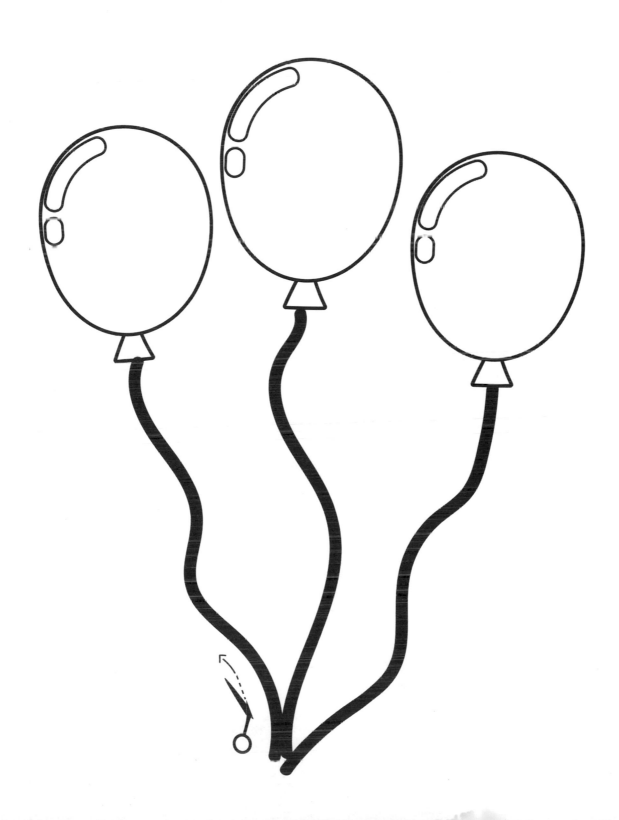

LET'S CUT ALONG:
SEAWEED

Practice cutting curvy lines as you cut along each seaweed.

LET'S CUT ALONG:
MAGIC WANDS

Practice cutting straight lines as you cut along each magic wand.

RACCOON WHISKERS

Practice cutting short lines as you cut along each raccoon whisker.

LET'S CUT ALONG:
PRACTICE LINES

Practice cutting zigzag lines.

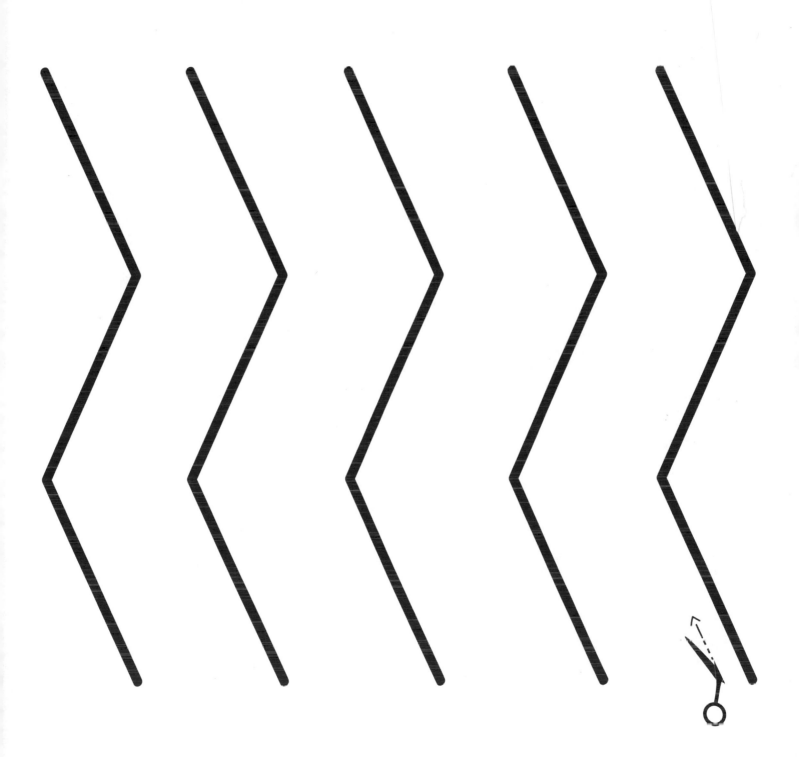

LET'S CUT ALONG:
PRACTICE LINES

Practice cutting zigzag lines.

THE CAT WHISKERS

Practice cutting short lines as you cut along each cat whisker.

LET'S CUT OUT:
SQUARES

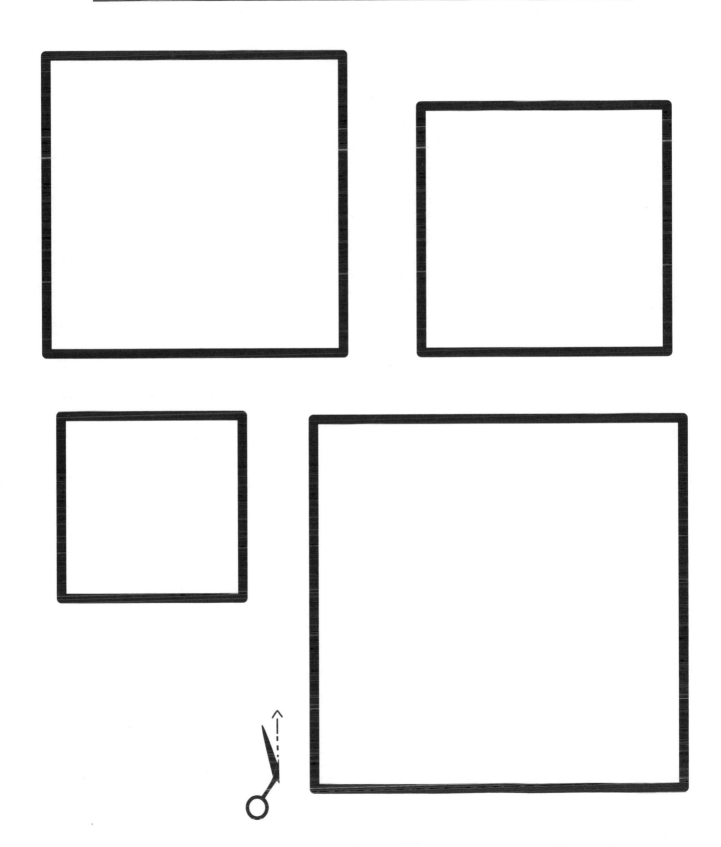

CiRCLES

TRIANGLES

RECTANGLES

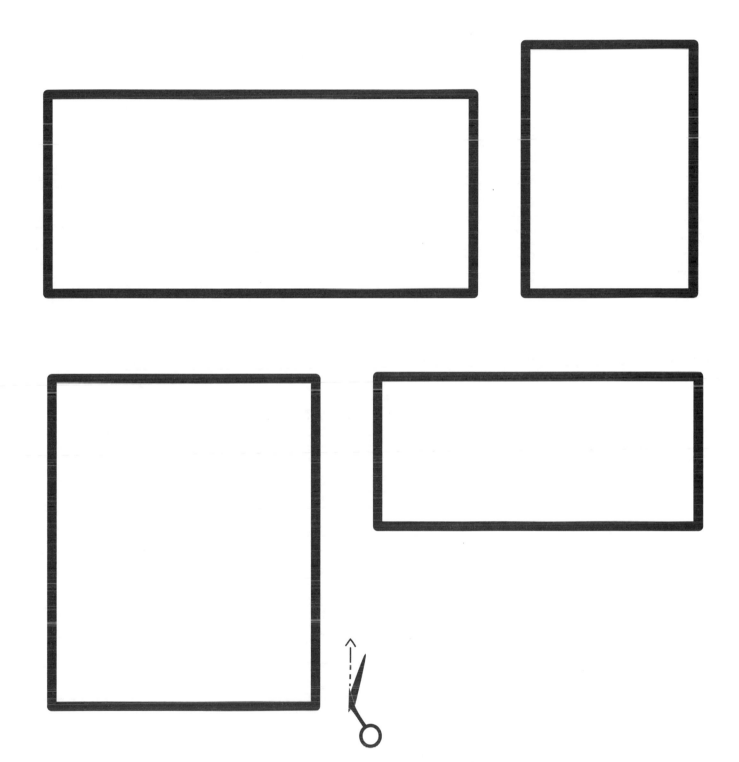

LET'S CUT OUT:
PENTAGONS

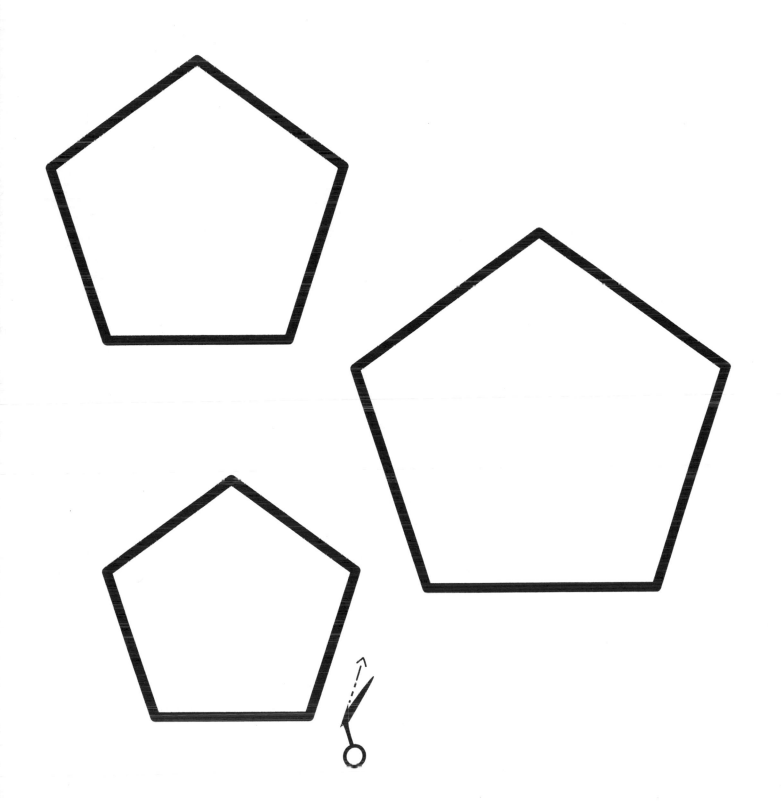

HEXAGONS

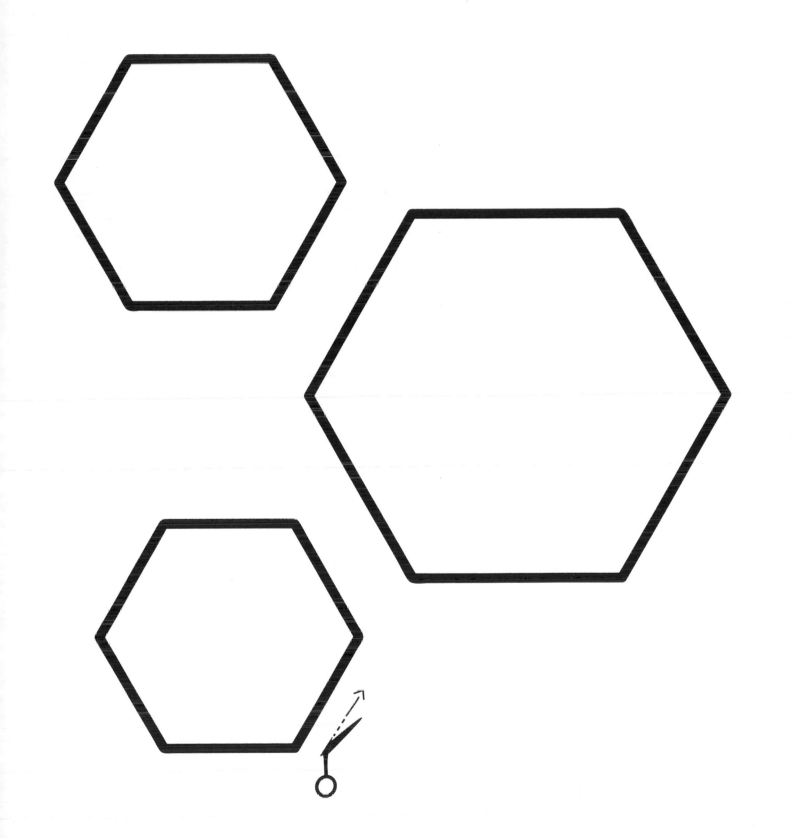

LET'S CUT OUT:
A SPIRAL

A BEAR

AN OWL

A MONKEY

A FOX

A COW

A TIGER

A RABBIT

A DOG

A GiRAFFE

A CASTLE

A HOUSE

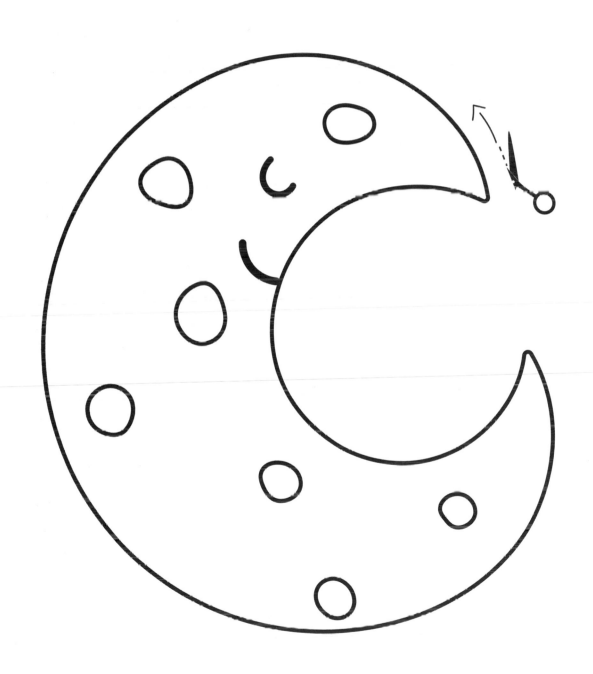

LET'S CUT OUT:
A SHOOTING STAR

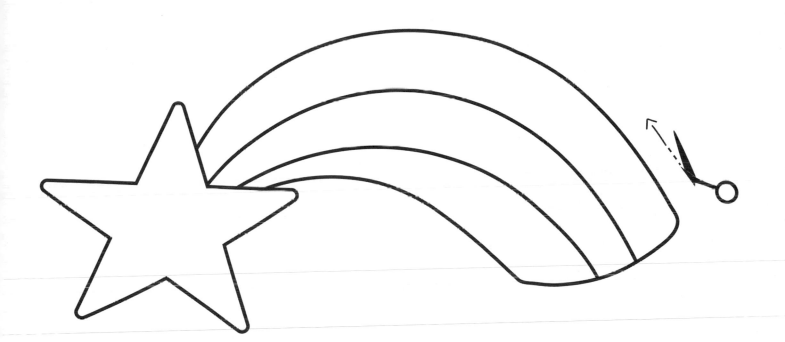

GEMS

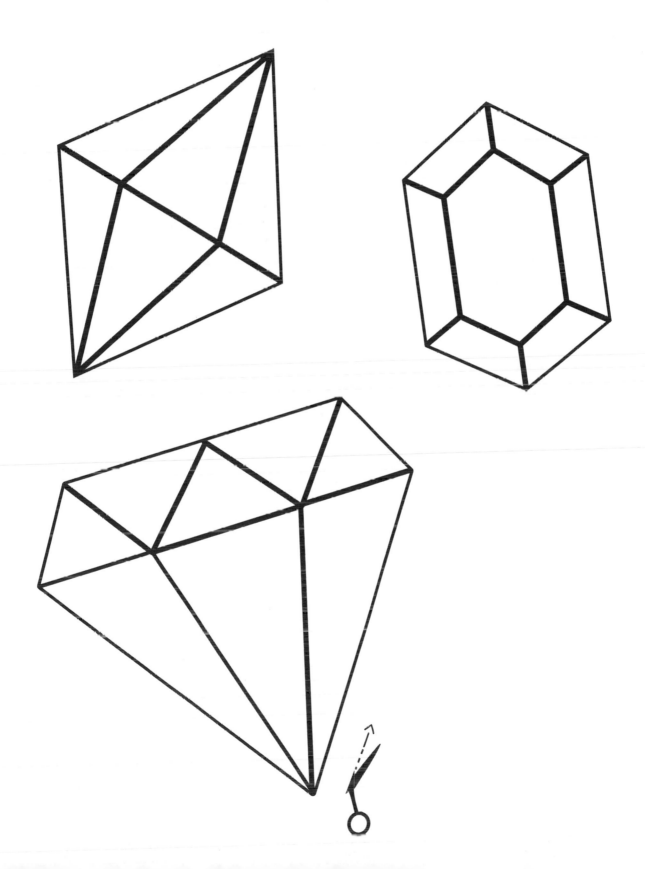

LET'S CUT OUT:
HEARTs

FLOWERS